The Old Fashioned Division Book

The no-nonsense
book of
practice in
basic division
(with answers)

Ward Lock Educational
47 Marylebone Lane
London W1M 6AX

50p

Note to the reader

Pencil in your answers lightly so that you can rub them out and practise again. You can check your answers at the back of the book.

Other titles in this series:

The Old Fashioned Times Table Book
ISBN 0 7062 3749 8

The Old Fashioned Adding-Up Book
ISBN 0 7062 4086 3

The Old Fashioned Taking-Away Book
ISBN 0 7062 4148 7

The Old Fashioned Multiplication Book
ISBN 0 7062 4121 5

The Old Fashioned Mental Arithmetic Book
ISBN 0 7062 4160 6

The Old Fashioned Handwriting Book
ISBN 0 7062 4139 8

The Old Fashioned Rules of Grammar Book
ISBN 0 7062 3850 8

The Old Fashioned Rules of Spelling Book
ISBN 0 7062 4085 5

© Ward Lock Educational Ltd

First published 1984
by Ward Lock Educational Ltd.
47 Marylebone Lane
London W1M 6AX

A Ling Kee Company

ISBN 0 7062 4122 3

Set by Style Photosetting Ltd, Tunbridge Wells, Kent.
Printed by Chigwell Press Oakwood Hill Loughton Essex IG10 3TZ

Divide these numbers.
The first one is done for you.

1. $9 \div 3 = 3$

2. $8 \div 2 = 4$

3. $6 \div 3 = 2$

4. $8 \div 4 = 2$

5. $12 \div 3 = 4$

6. $16 \div 2 = 8$

7. $14 \div 2 = 7$

8. $15 \div 5 = 3$

9. $20 \div 10 = 2$

10. $15 \div 3 = 5$

11. $24 \div 4 = 6$

12. $25 \div 5 = 5$

13. $30 \div 10 = 3$

14. $28 \div 4 = 7$

15. $18 \div 3 = 6$

16. $20 \div 5 = 4$

17. $27 \div 3 = 9$

18. $32 \div 4 = 8$

Divide these numbers.
The first one is done for you.

1. $21 \div 7 = 3$

2. $18 \div 6 =$

3. $24 \div 8 =$

4. $18 \div 9 =$

5. $24 \div 6 =$

6. $28 \div 7 =$

7. $32 \div 8 =$

8. $30 \div 6 =$

9. $27 \div 9 =$

10. $45 \div 9 =$

11. $40 \div 8 =$

12. $90 \div 9 =$

13. $72 \div 8 =$

14. $42 \div 7 =$

15. $49 \div 7 =$

16. $81 \div 9 =$

17. $35 \div 7 =$

18. $64 \div 8 =$

1. $21 \div 7 = 3$

2. $18 \div 6 =$

3. $24 \div 6 =$

4. $18 \div 9 =$

5. $24 \div 6 =$

6. $28 \div 7 =$

7. $32 \div 8 =$

8. $30 \div 6 =$

9. $27 \div 9 =$

10. $45 \div 9 =$

11. $40 \div 8 =$

12. $90 \div 9 =$

13. $72 \div 8 =$

14. $42 \div 7 =$

15. $49 \div 7 =$

16. $81 \div 9 =$

17. $35 \div 7 =$

18. $64 \div 8 =$

Write in the missing numbers.
The first one is done for you.

1. $20 \div \boxed{4} = 5$

2. $24 \div \boxed{} = 3$

3. $18 \div \boxed{} = 3$

4. $32 \div \boxed{} = 4$

5. $30 \div \boxed{} = 5$

6. $18 \div \boxed{} = 2$

7. $45 \div \boxed{} = 9$

8. $80 \div \boxed{} = 8$

9. $35 \div \boxed{} = 5$

10. $40 \div \boxed{} = 8$

11. $36 \div \boxed{} = 6$

12. $54 \div \boxed{} = 6$

13. $72 \div \boxed{} = 9$

14. $42 \div \boxed{} = 7$

15. $60 \div \boxed{} = 6$

16. $56 \div \boxed{} = 8$

17. $49 \div \boxed{} = 7$

Write in the missing numbers.
The first one is done for you.

1. $20 \div \boxed{} = 5$

2. $24 \div \boxed{} = 3$

3. $18 \div \boxed{} = 3$

4. $32 \div \boxed{} = 4$

5. $30 \div \boxed{} = 6$

6. $18 \div \boxed{} = 2$

7. $45 \div \boxed{} = 9$

8. $80 \div \boxed{} = 8$

9. $35 \div \boxed{} = 5$

10. $40 \div \boxed{} = 8$

11. $36 \div \boxed{} = 6$

12. $54 \div \boxed{} = 9$

13. $72 \div \boxed{} = 9$

14. $42 \div \boxed{} = 7$

15. $60 \div \boxed{} = 6$

16. $56 \div \boxed{} = 8$

17. $49 \div \boxed{} = 7$

You can also set out problems this way.

1. $2 \overline{)8}$ $\overset{4}{}$

2. $4 \overline{)12}$

3. $3 \overline{)15}$

4. $5 \overline{)25}$

5. $4 \overline{)12}$

6. $3 \overline{)27}$

7. $6 \overline{)24}$

8. $7 \overline{)21}$

9. $8 \overline{)32}$

10. $6 \overline{)54}$

11. $7 \overline{)49}$

12. $8 \overline{)64}$

13. $5 \overline{)30}$

14. $9 \overline{)63}$

1. 2)8 2. 4)12

3. 7)15 4. 5)25

5. 4)12 6. 3)27

7. 6)24 8. 7)21

9. 3)31 10. 6)54

11. 7)49 12. 8)60

13. 5)30 14. 9)63

Now you can divide larger numbers.

Divide the tens first then the units.

6 tens ÷ 3 = 2 tens $\quad$ $3\overline{)69}$ with 2 above

9 units ÷ 3 = 3 units $\quad$ $3\overline{)69}$ with 23 above

Now try these:

1. $2\overline{)48}$ $\qquad$ 2. $4\overline{)80}$

3. $3\overline{)93}$ $\qquad$ 4. $5\overline{)55}$

5. $4\overline{)84}$ $\qquad$ 6. $3\overline{)63}$

7. $2\overline{)64}$ $\qquad$ 8. $8\overline{)88}$

9. $3\overline{)99}$ $\qquad$ 10. $2\overline{)82}$

11. $4\overline{)48}$ $\qquad$ 12. $9\overline{)99}$

When a number will not divide exactly you have a *remainder*.

Look at this problem: $2\overline{)85}$

8 tens ÷ 2 = 4 tens

5 units ÷ 2 = 2 units
and 1 unit left over

$$42\,r1$$
$$2\overline{)85}$$

So the answer is 42, remainder 1.

Practise with these:

1. $4\overline{)46}$ 2. $3\overline{)62}$

3. $5\overline{)52}$ 4. $2\overline{)89}$

5. $7\overline{)75}$ 6. $8\overline{)83}$

7. $4\overline{)89}$ 8. $3\overline{)95}$

9. $2\overline{)61}$ 10. $8\overline{)84}$

Look at this problem: $3\overline{)72}$

7 tens ÷ 3 = 2 tens
with one ten left over.

$$3\overline{)72}^{2}$$

Now change the ten to 10 units.
With the 2 units you have
already, this gives you 12 units.

Write a little 1 in front
of the 2 units.

$$3\overline{)7^12}^{2}$$

It will remind you that you
have 12 units.

12 units ÷ 3 = 4 units.

$$3\overline{)7^12}^{24}$$

Now try these:

1. $4\overline{)56}$ 2. $3\overline{)45}$

3. $6\overline{)78}$ 4. $5\overline{)65}$

5. $8\overline{)96}$ 6. $7\overline{)84}$

7. $2\overline{)94}$ 8. $4\overline{)92}$

9. $5\overline{)60}$ 10. $3\overline{)75}$

11. $4\overline{)52}$ 12. $2\overline{)72}$

If there is more than 1 ten left over, change all the tens to units and show them like this:

$$3 \overline{)5^27} \quad \frac{19}{} \qquad 5 \overline{)8^35} \quad \frac{17}{}$$

Now try these:

1. $4 \overline{)64}$ 2. $5 \overline{)80}$

3. $3 \overline{)81}$ 4. $4 \overline{)68}$

5. $6 \overline{)96}$ 6. $7 \overline{)98}$

7. $3 \overline{)54}$ 8. $4 \overline{)76}$

9. $5 \overline{)95}$ 10. $3 \overline{)57}$

11. $6 \overline{)90}$ 12. $5 \overline{)85}$

13. $4 \overline{)72}$ 14. $3 \overline{)87}$

You can use the same method to divide hundreds, tens and units.

Look at this problem:

$$\frac{2\ \text{I}\ 5}{4\ )\ 8\ 6^20}$$

Now practise with these.

Divide the hundreds first, then the tens, then the units.

1. $3\ )\overline{6\ 9\ 3}$ 2. $5\ )\overline{5\ 2\ 5}$

3. $4\ )\overline{8\ 5\ 6}$ 4. $6\ )\overline{6\ 9\ 0}$

5. $7\ )\overline{7\ 1\ 4}$ 6. $4\ )\overline{4\ 7\ 2}$

7. $5\ )\overline{5\ 3\ 0}$ 8. $3\ )\overline{9\ 8\ 7}$

9. $2\ )\overline{6\ 5\ 6}$ 10. $8\ )\overline{8\ 7\ 2}$

11. $6\ )\overline{6\ 7\ 8}$ 12. $9\ )\overline{9\ 3\ 6}$

If there are any hundreds left over, change each hundred to 10 tens.

Look at these problems:

$$3\overline{)438} \qquad 6\overline{)954}$$

Your little numbers show that you have 13 tens and 18 units to divide.

$$\begin{array}{r} 146 \\ 3\overline{)4^13^18} \end{array}$$

Here the little numbers show that you have 35 tens and 54 units to divide.

$$\begin{array}{r} 159 \\ 6\overline{)9^35^54} \end{array}$$

Practise with these:

1. $4\overline{)564}$ 2. $7\overline{)882}$

3. $6\overline{)726}$ 4. $4\overline{)912}$

5. $5\overline{)730}$ 6. $3\overline{)822}$

7. $8\overline{)928}$ 8. $3\overline{)543}$

9. $6\overline{)924}$ 10. $5\overline{)980}$

11. $4\overline{)708}$ 12. $7\overline{)938}$

Now try these problems with remainders.

The first one is done for you.

1. $\quad 5\overline{)2\,3^37}$ $47\text{r}2$

2. $\quad 6\overline{)8\,2\,5}$

3. $\quad 3\overline{)8\,5\,3}$

4. $\quad 2\overline{)9\,1\,1}$

5. $\quad 7\overline{)3\,7\,6}$

6. $\quad 8\overline{)1\,1\,7}$

7. $\quad 9\overline{)3\,7\,4}$

8. $\quad 5\overline{)2\,2\,2}$

9. $\quad 6\overline{)5\,0\,2}$

10. $\quad 4\overline{)9\,6\,9}$

11. $\quad 7\overline{)8\,2\,0}$

12. $\quad 6\overline{)4\,4\,9}$

13. $\quad 3\overline{)5\,6\,8}$

14. $\quad 5\overline{)7\,7\,2}$

15. $\quad 6\overline{)8\,3\,1}$

16. $\quad 9\overline{)3\,3\,7}$

Answers

Page 1

1. 3	**2.** 4	**3.** 2	**4.** 2	**5.** 4	**6.** 8
7. 7	**8.** 3	**9.** 2	**10.** 5	**11.** 6	**12.** 5
13. 3	**14.** 7	**15.** 6	**16.** 4	**17.** 9	**18.** 8

Page 2

1. 3	**2.** 3	**3.** 3	**4.** 2	**5.** 4	**6.** 4
7. 4	**8.** 5	**9.** 3	**10.** 5	**11.** 5	**12.** 10
13. 9	**14.** 6	**15.** 7	**16.** 9	**17.** 5	**18.** 8

Page 3

1. 4	**2.** 8	**3.** 6	**4.** 8	**5.** 6	**6.** 9
7. 5	**8.** 10	**9.** 7	**10.** 5	**11.** 6	**12.** 9
13. 8	**14.** 6	**15.** 10	**16.** 7	**17.** 7	

Page 4

1. 4	**2.** 3	**3.** 5	**4.** 5	**5.** 3	**6.** 9
7. 4	**8.** 3	**9.** 4	**10.** 9	**11.** 7	**12.** 8
13. 6	**14.** 7				

Page 5

1. 24	**2.** 20	**3.** 31	**4.** 11	**5.** 21	**6.** 21
7. 32	**8.** 11	**9.** 33	**10.** 41	**11.** 12	**12.** 11

Page 6

1. 11r2	**2.** 20r2	**3.** 10r2	**4.** 44r1	**5.** 10r5
6. 10r3	**7.** 22r1	**8.** 31r2	**9.** 30r1	**10.** 10r4

Page 7

1. 14	**2.** 15	**3.** 13	**4.** 13	**5.** 12	**6.** 12
7. 47	**8.** 23	**9.** 12	**10.** 25	**11.** 13	**12.** 36

Page 8

1. 16	**2.** 16	**3.** 27	**4.** 17	**5.** 16	**6.** 14
7. 18	**8.** 19	**9.** 19	**10.** 19	**11.** 15	**12.** 17
13. 18	**14.** 29				

Page 9

1. 231	**2.** 105	**3.** 214	**4.** 115	**5.** 102	**6.** 118
7. 106	**8.** 329	**9.** 328	**10.** 109	**11.** 113	**12.** 104

Page 10

1. 141	**2.** 126	**3.** 121	**4.** 228	**5.** 146	**6.** 274
7. 116	**8.** 181	**9.** 154	**10.** 196	**11.** 177	**12.** 134

Page 11

1. 47r2	**2.** 137r3	**3.** 284r1	**4.** 455r1	**5.** 53r5	**6.** 14r5
7. 41r5	**8.** 44r2	**9.** 83r4	**10.** 242r1	**11.** 117r1	**12.** 74r5
13. 189r1	**14.** 154r2	**15.** 138r3	**16.** 37r4		